It's Easy To Pla

Lady GaGa

Wise Publications
part of The Music Sales Group

London / New York / Paris / Sydney / Copenhagen / Berlin / Madrid / Hong Kong / Tokyo

Published by
Wise Publications
14-15 Berners Street, London W1T 3LJ, UK.

Exclusive Distributors:
Music Sales Limited
Distribution Centre, Newmarket Road,
Bury St Edmunds, Suffolk IP33 3YB, UK.

Music Sales Pty Limited
20 Resolution Drive,
Caringbah, NSW 2229, Australia.

Order No. AM1001330
ISBN: 978-1-84938-654-8
This book © Copyright 2010 by Wise Publications.

Edited by Jenni Wheeler.
Cover designed by Liz Barrand.

Printed in the the EU.

Your Guarantee of Quality
As publishers, we strive to produce every book
to the highest commercial standards.
The music has been freshly engraved and the
book has been carefully designed to minimise
awkward page turns and to make playing from
it a real pleasure.
Particular care has been given to specifying acid-free,
neutral-sized paper made from pulps which have not
been elemental chlorine bleached.
This pulp is from farmed sustainable forests and was
produced with special regard for the environment.
Throughout, the printing and binding have been
planned to ensure a sturdy, attractive publication
which should give years of enjoyment.
If your copy fails to meet our high standards,
please inform us and we will gladly replace it.

www.musicsales.com

Alejandro

Words & Music by Stefani Germanotta & RedOne

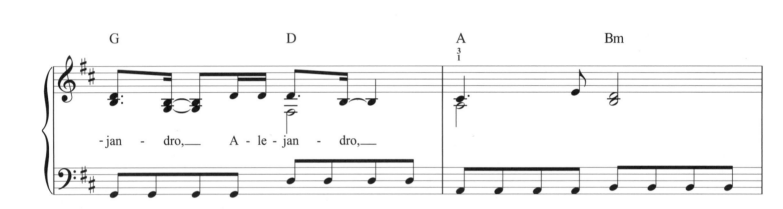

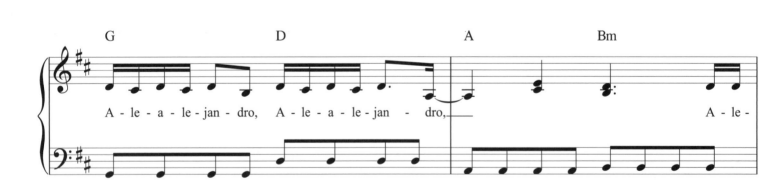

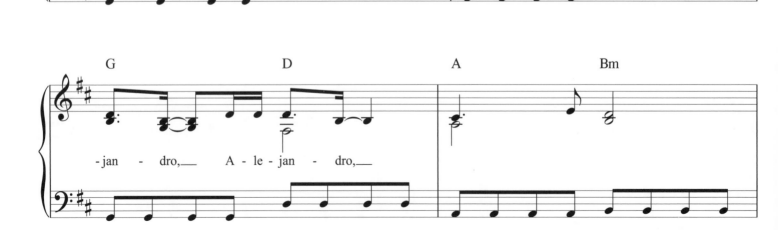

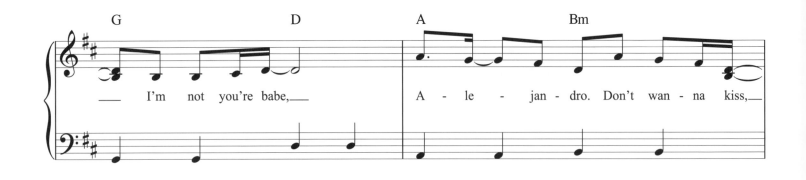

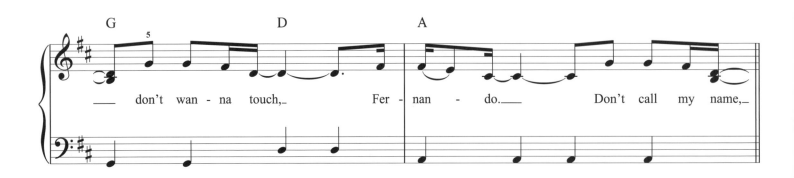

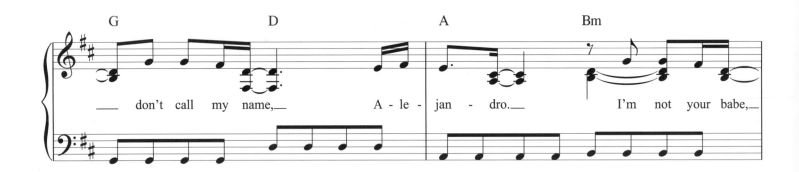

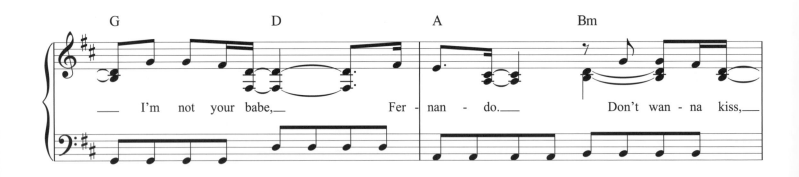

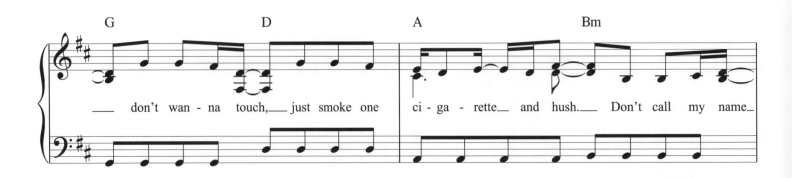

Bad Romance

Words & Music by Stefani Germanotta & RedOne

love, love, love. I want your love. (Love love, I want your love.)
love, love, love. I want your love.

Am

Spoken: *You know that I want you.*   *And you know that I need you.*   *I want it bad,   your*

Am/G   F   G

bad ro - mance.   I want your love and___ I   want your re - venge,___ you and me___

Am   C   F

___ could write a bad ro - mance.___   (Oh.)___   I want your love and all your

G   E/G#   Am

lo - vers' re - venge. You and me___ could write a bad ro - mance.___   Oh,___

12

Brown Eyes

Words & Music by Robert Fusari & Stefani Germanotta

18

19

Eh, Eh (Nothing Else I Can Say)

Words & Music by Martin Kierszenbaum & Stefani Germanotta

Eh, eh, eh, eh, eh, eh, eh, eh, eh, eh, hey. I

have some-thing that I love long, long but my friends keep a-tell-in' me that some-thin's wrong. Then I

met some-one and eh, there's noth-in' else I can say, eh,___ eh.___

There's noth-in' else I can say, eh,___ eh,___ there's noth-in' else I can

say, eh,___ eh.___ Wish you nev-er looked at me that way, eh,___ eh.___

___ I wish you nev-er looked at me that way, eh,___ eh.___ There's noth-in' else I can

say, eh,___ eh.___ I wish you nev-er looked at me that way, eh,___ eh.___

___ There's noth-in' else I can say, eh,___ eh.___ Cher-ry, cher-ry, boom, boom, eh,

eh, hey,___ oh yeah.___ All I can say is eh, eh.

Just Dance

Words & Music by Aliaune Thiam, Stefani Germanotta
& Nadir Khayat

26

27

D.S. al Coda

Coda

29

Money Honey

Words & Music by Nadir Khayat & Bilal Hajji

-N - E - Y,___ so sex - y, I...

2.

You know I 'pre - ci - ate the fin - er things,___ but it's not___

___ what makes me hap - pi - est, ba - by. (I can do with - out it,

babe.) Your ten - der lov - in's more than I can han - dle. Nev - er

burn out this can - dle, ba - by, ba - by._____ K - k - k -

The Fame

Words & Music by Martin Kierszenbaum & Stefani Germanotta

38

Poker Face

Words & Music by Stefani Germanotta & Nadir Khayat

40

Paparazzi

Words & Music by Robert Fusari & Stefani Germanotta

45

47

Speechless

Words & Music by Stefani Germanotta

Summerboy

Words & Music by Joshua Schwartz, Brian Kierulf
& Stefani Germanotta

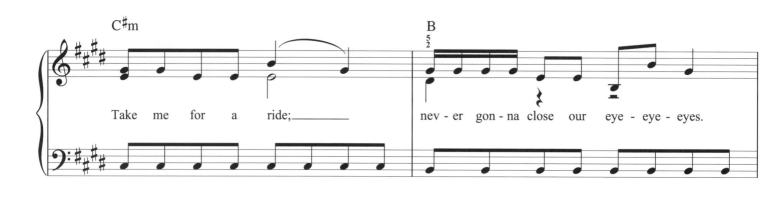

C#m Take me for a ride;_____ **B** nev - er gon - na close our eye - eye - eyes.

F#m7 *Spoken: Hey there, sum - mer - boy,* *I'm a busy girl.* **C#m** Don't have too much time,_____

B hur-ry up be-fore I change my mind. **F#m7** *Spoken:* *Hey there, sum - mer - boy,* I'm *tak-ing off my heels.*

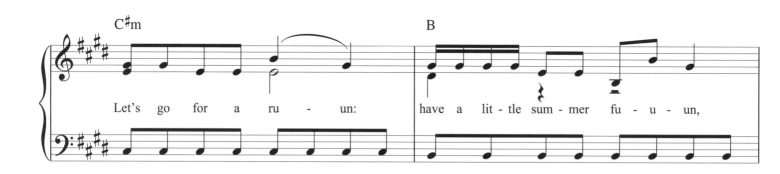

C#m Let's go for a ru - un: **B** have a lit-tle sum-mer fu - u - un,

N.C. *D.S. al Coda*

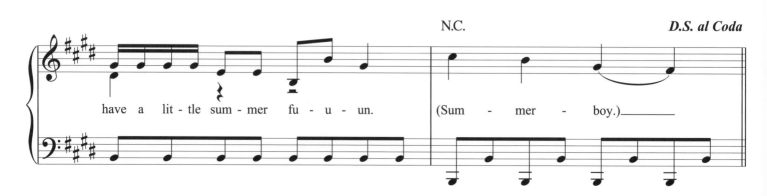

have a lit-tle sum-mer fu - u - un. (Sum - mer - boy.)_____

57

Telephone

Words & Music by Stefani Germanotta, Rodney Jerkins, LaShawn Daniels,
Lazonate Franklin & Beyoncé Knowles

59

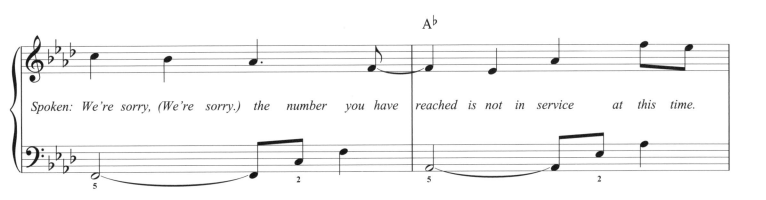

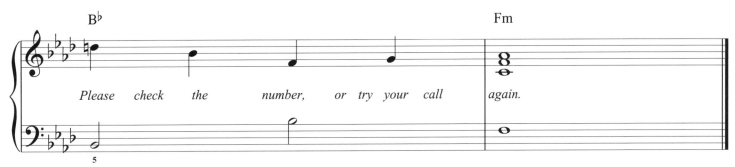

The 'It's Easy To Play' series offers you easy-to-read, simplified arrangements of music from the world's favourite performers and great composers. Ideal for beginners, the music is newly engraved and includes chord symbols and lyrics where appropriate.

Abba
AM22195

Bach
AM71721

Burt Bacharach
AM937497

Ballads
AM63025

The Beatles 1
NO17907

The Beatles 2
NO90342

Beethoven
AM71739

The Bee Gees
AM966790

Big Chart Hits
AM975161

Clayderman 1
AM61599

Clayderman 2
AM65921

Classic Film Themes
AM956241

Classical Chillout
AM988790

Classical Themes
AM31659

Classics 1
AM19563

Classics 2
AM60252

Coldplay X&Y
AM983477

Hymns
AM23698

Michael Jackson
AM77348

Jazz 1
AM15280

Elton John
AM61714

Norah Jones
AM977603

Jerome Kern
AM80268

Latin
AM18995

Love Songs
AM956220

Katie Melua
AM89584

Pop Hits
AM956219

Pops 1
AM27228

Pops 2
AM37904

Pops 3
AM65905

Pops 7
AM936441

Pops 8
AM952480

Pops 9
AM958848

Pops 10
AM963260

Songs Of England, Scotland & Ireland
AM31857

Spice Girls
AM956186

Sports Themes
AM955306

Cat Stevens
AM24274

Strauss
AM83791

Swing
AM20140

Tchaikovsky
AM82926

The Thirties
AM68313

The Forties
AM68321

Blues
AM15264

Blur
AM936265

Bon Jovi
AM936287

Boogie-Woogie
AM23706

Boyzone
AM966515

Mariah Carey
AM941985

The Carpenters
AM23342

Chart Hits
AM963259

Children's Songs
AM29489

Chopin
AM71747

Christmas Songs
AM22641

The Corrs
AM958815

Country 'n' Western
AM19530

Celine Dion
AM944042

Bob Dylan
AM78890

Duke Ellington
AM65939

Folk
AM18987

Gershwin
AM68511

Delta Goodrem
AM89442

Gospels
AM950390

Buddy Holly
AM90141

Whitney Houston
AM941480

More Jazz
AM62258

Movie Music
AM953865

Mozart
AM71754

New Film Themes
AM990154

New TV Themes
AM988339

90s Film Songs
AM956208

No.1 Hits
AM952501

Nursery Rhymes
AM37706

Oasis
AM936276

Roy Orbison
AM77363

Opera
AM32152

Piano Duets
AM62514

Popular Classics
AM952490

Popular Irish Music
AM958826

Pub Songs
AM69279

Ragtime
AM14143

Rock Hits
AM989175

Rock 'n' Roll
AM19555

Schubert
AM71762

Showstoppers
AM956230

Showtunes
AM26907

Paul Simon
PS10214

The Seventies
AM68354

The Nineties
AM944394

Top 50 Hits 1
AM95251

Top 50 Hits 2
AM952523

Top 50 Hits 3
AM958650

Top 50 Hits 4
AM958661

Paul Weller
AM942524

Waltzes
AM20421

Westlife
AM970409

Stevie Wonder
AM40007